At the Fun Fair

Dawn McMillan

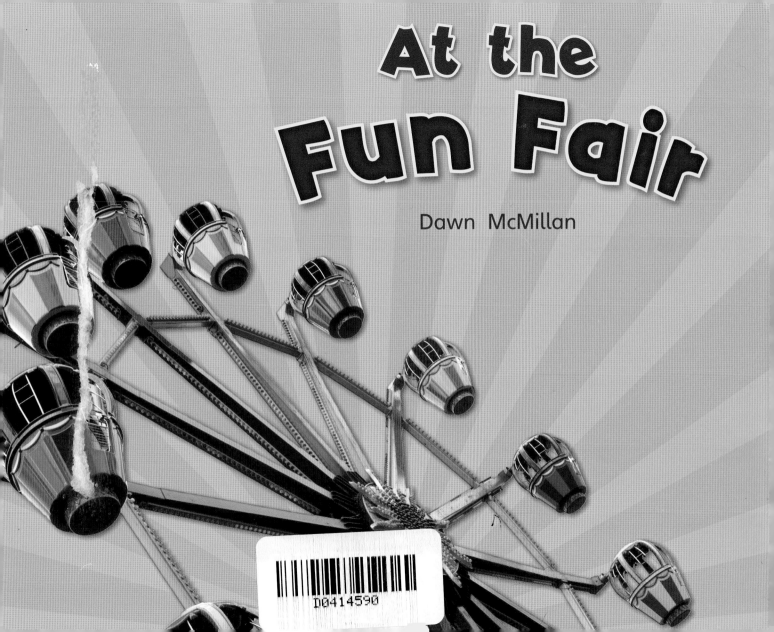

At the fun fair, we go up.

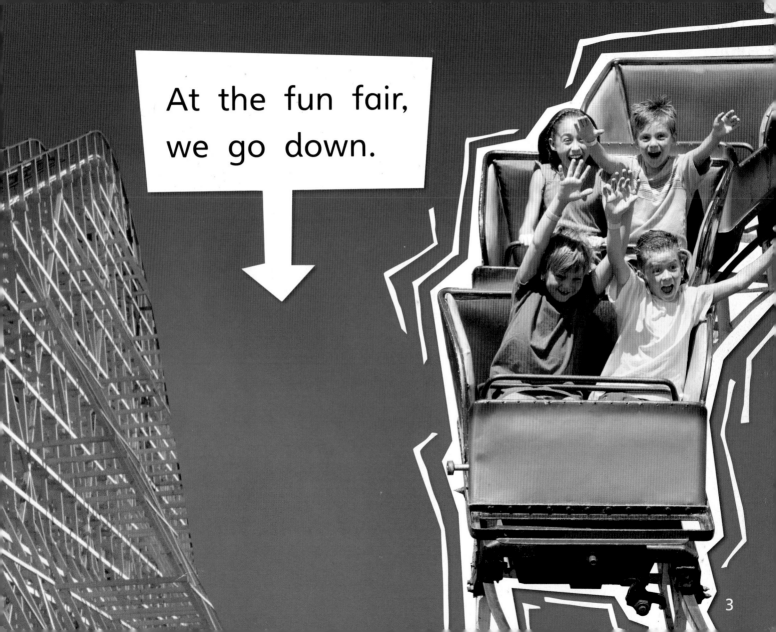

At the fun fair,
we go down.

3

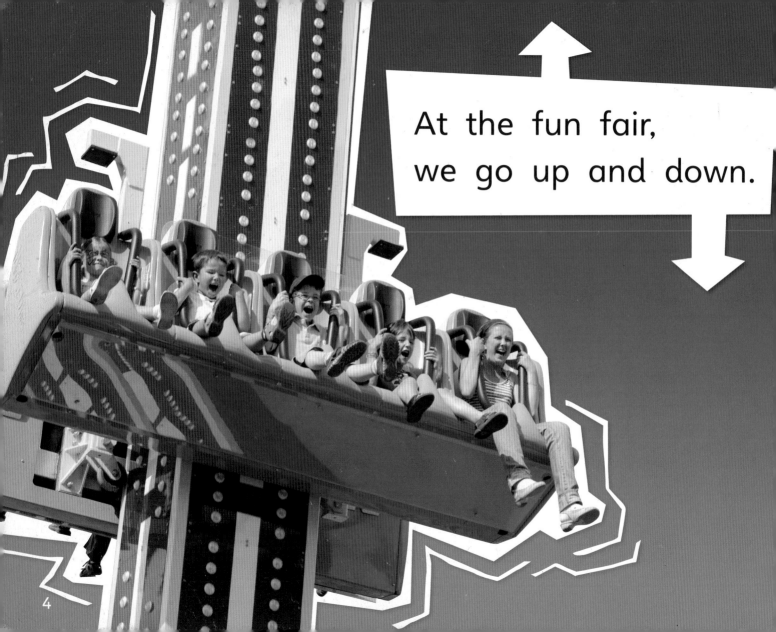

At the fun fair,
we go up and down.

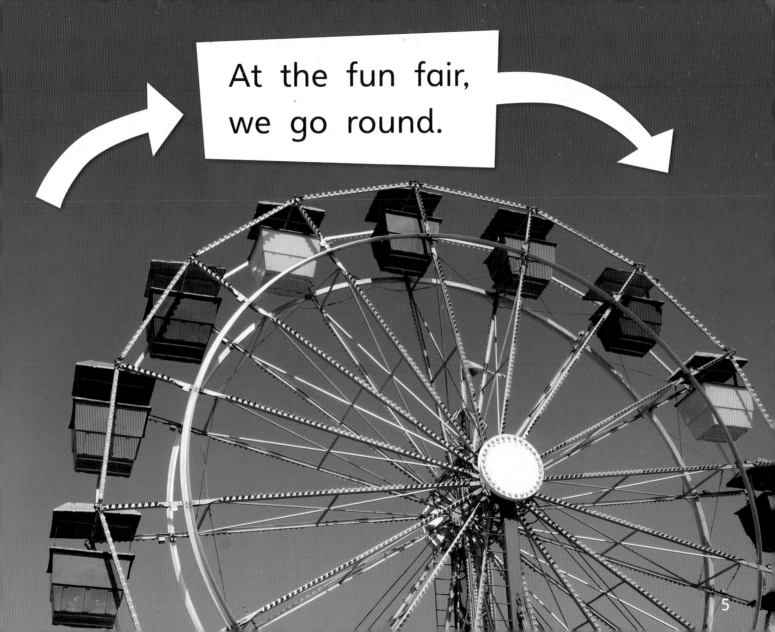

At the fun fair,
we go round.

5

At the fun fair,
we go round and round.

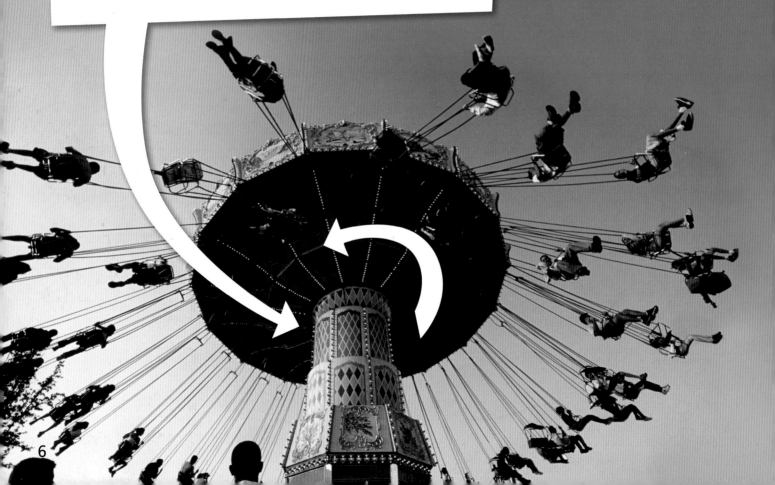

At the fun fair,
we go bump.

It is fun at the fun fair!